The Maths Calculator Book

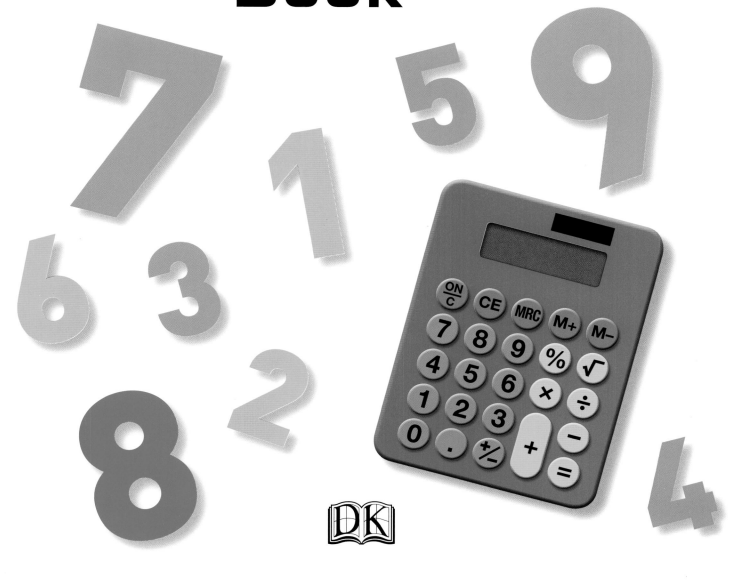

DK

DK

LONDON, NEW YORK, MUNICH,
MELBOURNE, and DELHI

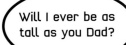

Will I ever be as tall as you Dad?

Read this book and find out.

Written by
Branka Surla and
Christian Dawson
Editor Steve Setford
Designer Peter Radcliffe
Publisher Laura Buller
Art Director & Jacket Designer Martin Wilson
Producer, Pre-Production Francesca Wardell
Producer Charlotte Cade
Publishing Director Sophie Mitchell

First published in Great Britain in 2014
by Dorling Kindersley Limited
80 Strand, London WC2R 0RL

Copyright © 2014 Dorling Kindersley Ltd
A Penguin Random House Company
2 4 6 8 10 9 7 5 3
005–195932–July/2014

A CIP catalogue record for this book
is available from the British Library.
ISBN: 978-1-4093-5410-9

Printed and bound in China
Calculator made in Hong Kong by Tritech

Discover more at **www.dk.com**

Picture credits
The publisher would like to thank the following
for their kind permission to reproduce their
photographs:

(Key: a-above; b-below/bottom; c-centre; f-far;
l-left; r-right; t-top)

12 Alamy Images: Ariadne Van Zandbergen (cr).
Dreamstime.com: Ivonne Wierink (crb).
15 Dreamstime.com: Peterfactors (cra).
19 Valeriy Kalyuzhnyy / StarJumper (c) Fotolia.
20 Alamy Images: Digifoto Gold (cr).
Dreamstime.com: Denys Kuvaiev (bl).
21 Dreamstime.com: Mark Herreid (b).
24 Alamy Images: S. T. Yiap / age fotostock (c).

25 Alamy Images: Jose Luis Stephens (b).
Jacket images: Front: Alamy Images:
Digifoto Gold (br); Graham Hughes (bl).
Corbis: Ocean (cr).

All other images © Dorling Kindersley
For further information see:
www.dkimages.com

CONTENTS

Meet your calculator

You've probably handled a calculator before, but how much do you actually know about using one correctly? To help you get started, here's a guide to using the simpler buttons on your calculator.

Solar panel
Your calculator does not need batteries, because it has a solar panel, which makes electricity from light.

CE button
This button Clears (deletes) the last Entry.

Display panel
This is where all your numbers and operations appear.

ON/C button
Press the ON/C button to turn on your calculator.

Press the ON/C button when you want to clear the display and start a new calculation.

+ − x ÷ buttons
Press one of these buttons if you want to add, subtract, multiply, or divide two numbers.

(Remember to press the = button to find out the answer.)

Examples:
9 + 9 = 18
43 − 17 = 26
14 x 15 = 210
169 ÷ 13 = 13

1 2 3 4 5 6 7 8 9 0 buttons
Press these whenever you want to input a number.

For example, if you want to input the number 347:

Press 3
Then 4
Then 7
The number 347 will appear on the display.

. (decimal point) button
Press this to include a decimal point.
For example, if you want to input 3.6:
Press 3
Then .
Then 6
The display panel will show 3.6.

= (equals) button
Use this button to find the answer when you're working out standard calculations:

• additions
• subtractions
• multiplications
• divisions

First steps

This is how you would normally see a mathematics question written down:

14 + 27 =

These are the buttons you need to press to calculate the answer:

You will see the answer appear on the display like this: 41

Now have a go at the examples below, which use all the buttons we've seen so far. (The answers are shown upside down at the foot of the page.)

1 + 2 + 3 + 4 + 5 + 6 + 7 + 8 + 9 =

(1) + (2) + (3) + (4) + (5) + (6) + (7) + (8) + (9) (=)

123 + 456 + 789 =

(1)(2)(3) + (4)(5)(6) + (7)(8)(9) (=)

987 − 654 − 321 =

(9)(8)(7) − (6)(5)(4) − (3)(2)(1) (=)

Star tip!
If you make a mistake and hit the wrong key, you can always delete the last number by pressing the CE button.

147 × 258 × 369 =

(1)(4)(7) × (2)(5)(8) × (3)(6)(9) (=)

Star tip!
Once you've got your answer, you'll need to press the ON/C button to clear the result so you can start the next calculation.

12345678 ÷ 9 =

(1)(2)(3)(4)(5)(6)(7)(8) ÷ (9) (=)

Answers: 1. 45   2. 1368   3. 12   4. 13994694   5. 1371742

5

The calculator has its own built-in memory. You can use it to store a number partway through a calculation, rather than having to write it down or remember it yourself for later. There are three different memory buttons.

M+ button

Press this to **add** a number to the number currently stored in your calculator's memory.

M− button

Press this to **subtract** a number from the number currently stored in your calculator's memory.

MRC button

Press this button once to recall the number stored in the memory.

Press it twice to clear the memory.

When a number is stored in the memory of your calculator, the word **MEMORY** appears on the display panel.

% (percentage) button

Press this button to find a percentage of a number, or to add or subtract percentages from a number.

+/− button

Press this button to make the number on the display positive or negative. If the number is already positive, this button will make it negative. If it is already negative, this button will make it positive. The word **MINUS** appears on the panel for negative numbers.

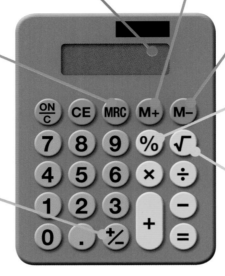

√ (square root) button

Press this button to find the square root of a number. The square root of a number we are working with is a number that, when multiplied by itself, gives us our original number.

For example, 3 is the square root of 9, because 3 x 3 = 9.

Have a go at these trickier examples ...

Example: (27 × 32) + (56 × 55) = ?

This needs to be done in two stages.

Work out 27 × 32 first and store the answer in the memory:

 864

Then work out 56 × 55 and add it to the memory:

 3080

To get the answer, press memory recall:

The answer will then be displayed: 3944

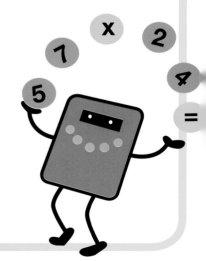

Percentage (%) calculations

You can do four different types of percentage calculation using the % button.

1. Calculate the percentage of a number.

Example: find 25% of 128

2. Increase a number by a certain percentage.

Example: increase 50 by 10%

3. Decrease a number by a certain percentage.

Example: decrease 360 by 5%

4. Calculate a fraction as a percentage.

Example: what is 12/240 as a percentage?

Square root (√) button

Example: find the square root of 81

Number crunch

Many of problems in this book are split into two sections: "the numbers" part gives you all the facts and figures you need, while "the crunch" part tells you what to do.

Look out also for "Star tips", which give useful formulas and equations.

Challenge rating!

Each question in this book has a coloured "traffic light" button beside it. The colour of the button shows how difficult the question is:

- green – an easier problem to start off
- amber – the next step up, a bit harder
- red – an extra-tough challenge to really test your skills.

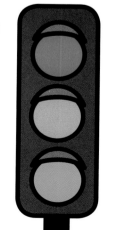

Trains, planes, and calculators
Don't let maths trip you up. Use your calculator to solve these tricky transport puzzles. Let's go!

On the right track

the crunch

- What is the total journey time of the five trains shown below?
- Calculate the average number of passengers that travelled on the five trains.
- What is the average journey time of the five trains?

the numbers

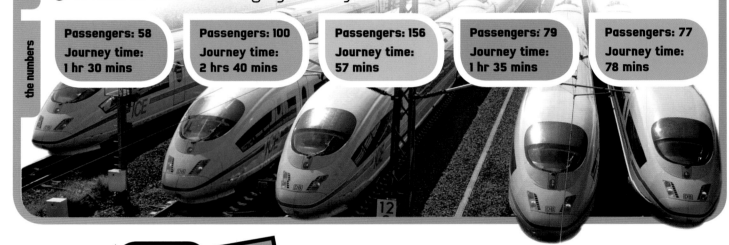

Passengers: 58	Passengers: 100	Passengers: 156	Passengers: 79	Passengers: 77
Journey time: 1 hr 30 mins	Journey time: 2 hrs 40 mins	Journey time: 57 mins	Journey time: 1 hr 35 mins	Journey time: 78 mins

Sky-high sums

the numbers

London to New York	
Plane fact	**Amount**
Speed	800 kph
Weight of plane	80,000 kg
Passengers	300
Fuel consumption per hour	3,600 litres
1st Class ticket price	£3,000
Business Class ticket price	£2,000
Economy Class ticket price	£500
Distance to New York	5,600 km
Average weight of passenger	70 kg

the crunch

Using the information in the table on the left, try to answer these questions:

- How long does it take to fly to New York?
- How many litres of fuel are needed to reach New York?
- What is the total weight of the plane and all the passengers?
- If 10% of the passengers travel 1st Class, 25% Business Class, and the rest Economy Class, how much would total ticket sales be?

Wheely cool

the crunch

● How many calories of energy do you burn on a 30 km bike ride?

● If a bicycle wheel's diameter is 622 mm, what is the wheel's circumference?

● How many times does the wheel go round in 1 km?

the numbers

Cycling burns 21.3 calories per km.

Circumference = π ("pi") x diameter

Star tip!
π (pi) is equal to 3.142

Mission to Mars

Have you ever dreamed of travelling to another planet or solar system? Let's start with a trip to Mars!

Mars

Trip takes 161 days

Earth

You'll need to eat three meals and drink 2 litres of water a day.

Radio waves travel at 300,000 km per second

Rocket travels at 14,000 km per hour

the numbers

the crunch

Using the diagram above, solve these problems with your calculator.

● How many meals will you need for the journey to Mars?

● How many litres of water will you need to travel to Mars and back?

● How far is it from Earth to Mars?

● How long will it take to send a message back to Earth from Mars?

Star tip!
Speed = Distance ÷ Time

9

Marvellous mind-bogglers

Are you ready to get your mind buzzing?
Try these brilliantly baffling brain teasers.

Consecutive numbers

- 812 is the product of two consecutive numbers. What are the two numbers?

- 336 is the product of three consecutive numbers. What are the three numbers?

- 140,556 is the product of three consecutive numbers. What are the three numbers?

- What is the largest number you can make pressing only these keys once: 1, 2, 3, 4, 5, 6, x, = ?

Heavy money

- A £20 note weighs 1 g. How heavy would 2 million pounds weigh if it was all made up of £20 notes?

Minute millionaire?

- Is it true that you have been alive for one million minutes?

Reversing Reversing

● Enter any two digits into the calculator, the largest first. Enter the digits again and then again, to make a six-digit number. For example:

95   9595   959595

What number do you have to subtract from this to get the order of the six digits reversed – so to get 595959 in the example above?

Try this with other two-digit combinations. What do you notice about the number you are subtracting each time?

Root of the problem

● The area of a square vegetable patch is 2.56 m². What is the length of each side in metres?

BEWARE!

Decimal dilemma

● The decimal equivalent of 1/6 is 0.1666666 (1 ÷ 6). And 1/2 is 0.5 (1 ÷ 2) in decimals.

If your calculator shows that **1/3** is **0.3333333**, and **2/3** is **0.6666666**, does **3/3** equal **0.9999999**?

A million to 7

● Start by putting 1 million into the calculator. Then, using only the **7**, **+**, **−**, **x**, **÷**, or **=** keys as many times as you like, try and reduce this number to **7**.

Zoo-keeper's conundrums

Have you ever thought about running your own zoo? There's more to it than meets the eye.

Feed me – cats with big appetites!

the numbers

Big cat: lion
Meat required:
6.8 kg per day
Number of
cats: 5

Big cat: cheetah
Meat required:
19 kg per week
Number of
cats: 7

Big cat: tiger
Meat required:
5.4 kg per day
Number of
cats: 3

Big cat: puma
Meat required:
4.7 kg per day
Number of
cats: 4

Big cat: jaguar
Meat required:
20.2 kg per week
Number of
cats: 4

the crunch

● How much will it cost to feed the lions for a week?

● How much will it cost to feed all the big cats for a week?

● What will the big cat food bill be for a whole year?

● If the price of meat goes up by 5%, what is the new annual meat cost?

> Meat costs £7.50 per kilogram!

How many bags full?

the numbers

Adult elephants produce 80 kg of dung each day. An elephant calf produces 40% of this amount. The zoo sells bags of elephant dung as fertilizer.

the crunch

● How much dung do the zoo's seven adult elephants produce in a week?

● How much dung do the zoo's three elephant calves produce in a week?

● How many full bags of dung are produced per week by the zoo if each bag holds 25 kg of dung?

Penguin pool puzzle

the numbers

We are building an enclosure for our cute penguins. Their pool will be 5 m long x 3 m wide x 1.3 m deep. There will be a fence around the pool, 1 metre away from the water's edge.

the crunch

● How large is the pool in cubic metres (m³)?

● How many litres of water will it hold if it is filled right up to the top? (1 cubic metre = 1,000 litres.)

● How many litres are needed to fill 60% of the pool?

● How many fence panels are needed to enclose the pool if each panel is 1.8 metres long?

● How much will it cost to build the fence if one fence panel costs £12?

3 m

1.3 m deep

1 m

5 m

Star tip
Volume = Length x Width x Depth

Tall tales...

the numbers

A fully grown giraffe is 5.5 metres tall. When they are born, giraffes are 2 metres in height.

Remember how to work out percentages? (See page 7.)

the crunch

● How much shorter is a baby giraffe compared with a fully grown adult giraffe?

● What percentage of its adult height is a giraffe at birth?

● How much does a giraffe grow on average per day if it takes two years to grow to full height?

Patterns and puzzles
Discover amazing number patterns with your calculator. Get pressing those buttons!

Ones and elevens

● What's the next step
in this pattern?
11 x 11 = 121
111 x 111 = 12321

I suppose he'll grow into it!

● Carry on this pattern
as far as you can go:
11 x 111   = 1221
11 x 1111 = 12221

Whatever next 1?
● Complete these
calculations:
9 X 9 =
98 X 9 =
987 X 9 =
9876 X 9 =
98765 X 9 =

What do
you think
comes next?

Whatever next 2?
● Try these problems:
9 – 1 =
98 – 21 =
987 – 321 =
9876 – 4321 =
98765 – 54321 =

What comes next?

Squares

What have the answers got in common?

$11^2 =$

$22^2 =$

$26^2 =$

$101^2 =$

$111^2 =$

$121^2 =$

$202^2 =$

$212^2 =$

$264^2 =$

$307^2 =$

$836^2 =$

$1001^2 =$

$1111^2 =$

$2002^2 =$

$2285^2 =$

$2636^2 =$

Star tip!
Squared numbers are numbers multiplied by themselves.

Sum and product

When two different numbers are added together, they give the sum of 10. When they are multiplied together, the same two numbers give a product of 20. What are the two numbers?

Find those consecutives!

What are the three consecutive numbers that add up to:

(a) **171**, (b) **210**, (c) **258**?

What are the two consecutive numbers with a product of **1332**?

Pick a pair

Make two numbers using a pair of digits (excluding zero) that are on top of each other on the calculator. Take the smallest from the largest.

For example:

$74 - 47 =$

$52 - 25 =$

$63 - 36 =$

What do you notice?

Make a pair of numbers using any two digits. Add them together.
For example:

$20 + 02 =$

$84 + 48 =$

$73 + 37 =$

Notice anything?

15

The great bake

We all enjoy tucking into a yummy cake or biscuit. But lots of calculations are needed to put on a bake sale. Get stuck into these tasty problems!

All tied up

the numbers

We've baked 20 cakes for our cake sale. Of these, three are 30 cm in diameter, five are 25 cm in diameter, and the rest are 18 cm in diameter. We want to put ribbon around each cake, with a 1-cm overlap where the ends meet.

the crunch

- How many cakes are 18 cm in diameter?
- What percentage of the cakes are 30 cm in diameter?
- How many metres of ribbon do we need altogether?

How do you work out the circumference of a circle? (See page 9.)

Pie-portion puzzler

the numbers

Jess makes some apple pies for the bake sale. She wants to cut each pie into eight portions and charge £1.35 per portion.

the crunch

- How much money will Jess make on one pie?
- If Jess increases the price of a portion by 20%, how much will she now charge per portion?
- If she increases the original price by 20% (as above) but cuts a pie into 12 portions, how much more money will she make on each pie?

Cookie challenge

the numbers

We have the ingredients for 90 chocolate chip cookies:

450 g butter, 480 g sugar, 675 g flour, 3 eggs, 600 chocolate chips

the crunch

● What is the combined weight of the butter, sugar, and flour?

● What's the average number of chocolate chips per cookie?

● Unfortunately, we have only 2 eggs in the fridge. How much of each ingredient should we now use to keep the proportions the same?

Cupcakes

the numbers

You burn 95 calories for every 1 kilometre you run. Using the information below, answer the following brain-teasers.

Low-fat cupcake: 132 calories

Normal cupcake: 300 calories

the crunch

● How many more calories are there in a normal cupcake than in a low-fat cupcake?

● If you eat three low-fat cupcakes and two-and-a-half normal cupcakes, how many calories will you consume in total?

● How much further do you need to run to burn off the extra calories you get from eating two normal cupcakes compared with eating two low-fat cupcakes?

Flapjack profit

the numbers

It costs £5.50 to buy all the ingredients needed to make 20 flapjacks.

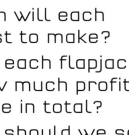

the crunch

● How much will each flapjack cost to make?

● If we sell each flapjack for 50p, how much profit will we make in total?

● How much should we sell each flapjack for in order to make 20% profit?

Out of this world!

These cosmic calculator tricks will bamboozle friends and show them you're a real maths star!

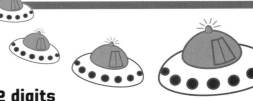

Mind reading

Pick 1 digit

● Ask a friend to pick a number between 1 and 9. Get him to multiply that number by 9 and then by 12,345,679.

When he shows you the result, you can tell him his original number!

Pick 3 digits

● Get a friend to pick a three-digit number, such as 437 or 842.

Ask her what the number is.

Get her to times it by 7, then by 11, then by 13.

Tell her you already know the answer!

Pick 2 digits

● Get a friend to pick a two-digit number, such as 38 or 67.

Ask her to tell you what the number is.

Get her to use the calculator to multiply her number by 3, then by 7, then by 13, and finally by 37.

Tell her you already know the answer!

An even trickier trick ...

● This trick is more difficult to master, but will totally amaze!

Get a friend to pick a two-digit number, such as 22 or 83.

Ask him what the number is.

Get him to use the calculator to multiply the number he chose by 3367.

Tell him you already know the answer!

How does he do that?

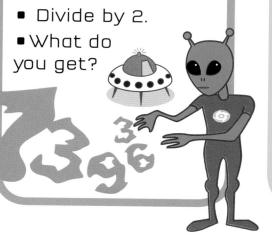

Extraterrestrial tricks

Trick 1

● **Step 1** Think of a number.

Step 2 Multiply it by 3.

Step 3 Add 6.

Step 4 Divide it by 3.

Step 5 Finally, subtract the number you thought of at the start.

Trick 2

● **Step 1** Think of a number.

Step 2 Double the number.

Step 3 Add 9.

Step 4 Subtract 3.

Step 5 Divide by 2.

Step 6 Subtract your original number.

Try these tricks using different numbers. What do you notice about the answers?

Seven-digit surprise!

● Think of a seven-digit number.

• Take the first three digits and times them by 80.

• Add 1.

• Multiply by 250.

• Add the last four digits of the original number twice.

• Subtract 250.

• Divide by 2.

• What do you get?

Golden numbers

● 1. Write two whole numbers on a sheet of paper, one above the other.

2. Add these two numbers together. Write the total on the line underneath.

3. Then total the last two numbers. Write the new number down underneath.

4. Keep going until you have 25 numbers in a list.

5. Choose any one of the last five numbers on the list, then divide it by the number above.

6. The answer is always 1.6180339!

Ever heard of the golden ratio? (See page 30.)

$$\begin{array}{r} 2\,9 \\ +\,4\,7 \\ \hline 7\,6 \\ \hline 1\,2\,3 \\ \hline 1\,9\,9 \end{array}$$

19

School Sports Day

Competition is fierce on Sports Day. These puzzles are sure to exercise your mind!

Keep hydrated!

the numbers

The PE teacher must give each of the 488 children taking part a drink.

He buys bottles of orange squash to dilute. Each cup of drink needs 25 millilitres (ml) of squash diluted with 300 ml of water. Each bottle of squash holds 75 centilitres (cl).

How many centilitres and millilitres in a litre? (See page 32.)

the crunch

● How many litres of undiluted squash does the teacher need if each child has one drink?

● In total, how many litres of diluted drink are made?

● How many bottles of undiluted orange squash does he buy?

On your marks!

the numbers

The fastest middle-distance runner in the school runs at 26 km per hour.

She burns 95 calories per kilometre.

Star tip!
Distance = Speed × Time

the crunch

● How far would she run in one quarter of an hour?

● How many calories does our runner burn in 800 metres?

● How long would it take to run 1 km at this pace in minutes and seconds?

Big throw

the numbers

The average throw of a javelin on Sports Day is 24 m.

There are 37 children taking part, and I have to pick up all the javelins!

the crunch

● If a javelin is 1.2 metres long, how many javelin lengths is the average throw?

● How far does the PE teacher have to walk in the afternoon to retrieve all the javelins?

● The winning throw of the javelin is 10% further than the second-placed throw. The second-placed throw is 6% further than the third-placed throw. If the third-placed throw is 32 metres, how far is the winning throw?

Long leap

the numbers

The triple jump is a hop, a skip, and then a jump. The winning distance is 12.8 metres. The hop is 35% of the total distance. The skip is 5/6 of the distance of the hop.

the crunch

● Find the distance of the hop, the skip, and the jump.

High jump

the numbers

The third-placed contestant jumps 7/8 of the height of the second-placed jumper. The second-placed jump is 15/16 of the winning jump. The winner jumps 160 cm.

the crunch

● Added together, how high do all three competitors jump in metres?

21

Be a calculator detective!

Use your calculator to make coded messages and solve mysteries. You'll soon be a super sleuth!

Writing with numbers

● Calculators can make words as well as do maths. Enter a few numbers and turn your calculator upside down. Do any look like letters? How many words can you make? Try sending coded messages to friends using calculator writing!

Some useful numbers: 0 = O 1 = I 2 = Z
3 = E 4 = h 5 = S 6 = g 7 = L 8 = B

Birthday sleuth

● Reveal a friend's date of birth with this astounding trick!

Give your calculator to a friend.

Ask her to add 18 to her birth month.

Multiply the answer by 25.

Subtract 333 and multiply by 8.

Subtract 554 and divide by 2.

Add her birth date day.

Multiply by 5 and add 692.

Multiply the answer by 20.

Add only the last two digits of her birth year.

Lastly, ask her to subtract 32940.

The answer will be the month first, then the day, and then the year of her birthday.

I can tell your age

● This trick works if the person is older than nine.

Step 1 Give your calculator to a friend. Ask him to multiply the first digit of his age by five, then add three. Now double the result and add the second digit of his age.

Step 2 Ask him to show you the total. Pretend you're concentrating hard on complicated sums, but just subtract six and you'll have his age!

How do you keep so young looking?

Symbols mystery

● Find all the missing operations to complete the calculations. Select from **+**, **−**, **×**, or **÷**.

(37 ☐ 21) ☐ 223 = 1000

(756 ☐ 18) ☐ 29 = 1218

27 ☐ (36 ☐ 18) = 675

31 ☐ (87 ☐ 19) = 2108

We're counting on you to crack the case!

● Using the digits 1, 2, 3, 4, and 5, complete the multiplications:

☐☐☐ × ☐☐ = 5535

☐☐☐ × ☐☐ = 3185

☐☐☐ × ☐☐ = 22032

● Using 3, 6, 8, and 9, complete the calculations:

☐☐ + ☐☐ = 125

107 − ☐☐ = ☐☐

All the fun of the fair!

The fair's in town! Why not take a spin on one of the rides or try your hand at some of the games?

You're on a roll!

the numbers

A brand new car is the amazing prize on one of the fairground stalls. To win it, you have to throw 6 dice at the same time and all of them need to land on 6.

the crunch

● What is the chance of winning the new car with one throw?

The chance of throwing a certain number on a dice is 1 in 6, or 1/6.

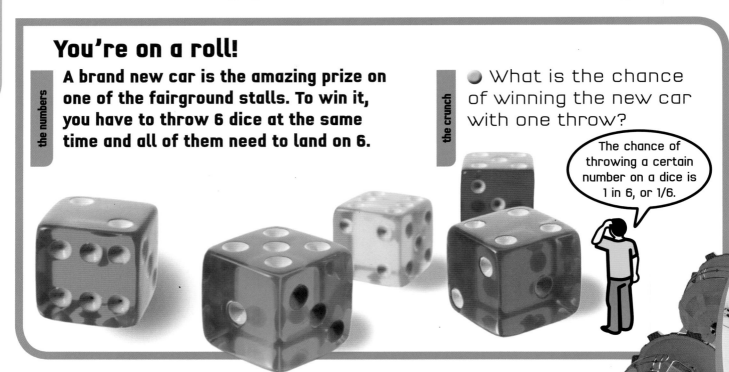

Spend, spend, spend!

the crunch

● How much is the candyfloss?

● How much does a ride on the ghost train cost?

● How much is it for a go on the waltzer?

● You have £20 to spend at the fair. How much change will you get if you have two goes on the dodgems, three goes on the ghost train, one go on the waltzer, and then buy candyfloss for yourself and each of your three friends?

the numbers

Attraction	Cost
Dodgems	£1.20
Ghost train	25% less than the dodgems
Waltzer	1/6 more than the dodgems
Candyfloss	1/3 of dodgems

Fancy your chances?

One of the most popular games at the fairground involves picking numbered balls out of a hat. The hat contains eight balls numbered from 1 to 8.

- If you pick out one ball from the hat, what are your chances of picking out ball number 2?
- If you pick out three balls, what are your chances of picking out balls 1, 2, and 3 in that order?
- What are your chances of picking out balls 1, 2, and 3 in any order?

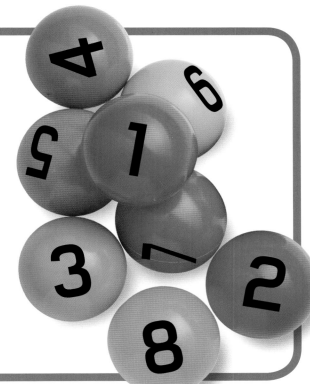

How do you work out the circumference? (See page 9.)

Big wheel, big thrills

The big wheel has 15 pods to ride in, and it can carry 75 people when it is full. The wheel has a radius of 5 metres. Each ride lasts for 5 minutes, during which the wheel spins round 30 times.

- How many people can fit into each pod?
- On a 5-minute ride, how far do you travel in total?
- How fast do you travel in kilometres per hour (kph) during the 5-minute ride?

Can you remember how to work out speed? (See page 9.)

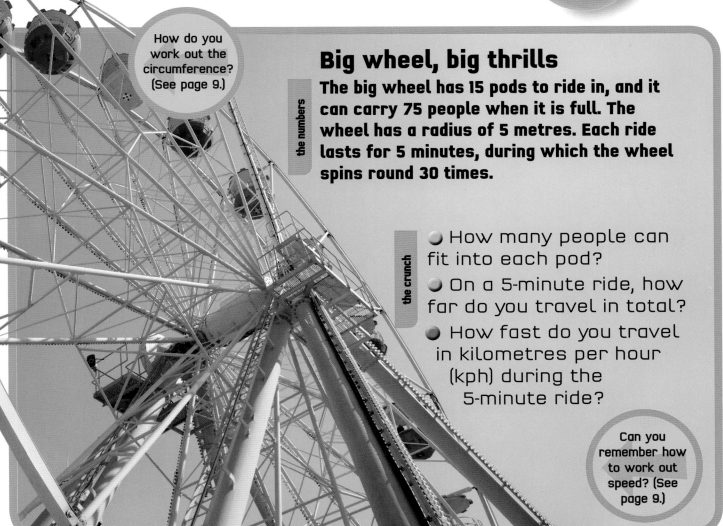

How to work things out
Check your answers here, and discover how all those amazing tricks and teasers work.

pages 8-9 Trains, planes, and calculators
On the right track

• Convert the journey times to minutes and add them together (1 hour = 60 minutes):
90 + 160 + 57 + 95 + 78 = 480 minutes

This total needs to be converted back into hours and minutes, so:
480 ÷ 60 = 8 hours exactly.

• Add up the total passenger numbers:
58 + 100 + 156 + 79 + 77 = 470 passengers

Divide 470 by 5, which gives an average of 94 passengers per train.

• Divide the journey times total of 480 minutes by 5. This gives an average journey time of 96 minutes – or 1 hour and 36 minutes.

Sky-high sums

• Time = Distance ÷ Speed, so:
5,600 km ÷ 800 kph = 7 hours

• Multiply the journey time by the fuel consumption per hour:
7 x 3,600 = 25,200 litres of fuel

• Multiply the average weight of a passenger by the number of passengers, then add the weight of the plane:
(300 x 70 kg) + 80,000 kg = 101,000 kg

• To calculate total takings:
(300 x 3000 x 10%) + (300 x 2000 x 25%) + (300 x 500 x 65%)
= 90,000 + 150,000 + 97,500 = £337,500

Mission to Mars

• 161 days x 3 meals = 483 meals

• 161 days x 2 litres x 2 (there and back) = 644 litres

• Distance = Speed x Time, so:
14,000 km per hour x 24 hours x 161 days = 54,096,000 km

• Time = Distance ÷ Speed, so:
54,096,000 ÷ 300,000 = 180.32 seconds,

which is approximately 3 minutes.
So it would take 6 minutes to send and receive back a message from Mars.

Wheely cool

• If you burn 21.3 calories every kilometre, to cycle 30 km:
30 x 21.3 = 639 calories burned

• Using the formula π x diameter:
3.142 x 622 = 1,954.324 mm (about 1.954 m)

• There are 1,000 metres in a kilometre, so:
1,000 ÷ 1.954 m = 511.77072 times (that's approximately 512 times)

pages 10-11 Marvellous mind-bogglers
Consecutive numbers

• 812 is the product of 28 and 29.

• 336 is the product 6, 7, and 8.

• 140,556 is the product of 51, 52, and 53.

This is a case of trial and improvement until you reach the correct numbers!

Heavy money

• £2,000,000 ÷ 20 = 100,000 notes
100,000 notes x 1 g = 100,000 g

There are 1,000 grams in a kilogram, so: 100,000 ÷ 1,000 = 100 kg

Minute millionaire?

• An 8-year-old child, for example, has been alive for:
8 x 365 days = 2,920 days
2,920 x 24 hours = 70,080 hours
70,080 x 60 minutes = 4,204,800 minutes!

1, 2, 3, 4, 5, 6, x, = keys

• You may think that working out the question methodically, as shown below, will help you find the answer more quickly:
65432 x 1 = 65,432

6543 x 21 = 137,403
654 x 321 = 209,934
65 x 4321 = 280,685
6 x 54321 = 325,926
However, the answer is 631 x 542 = 342,002!

Reversing

• The answer is always the difference between the two digits multiplied by 90909.

For example, if we choose 63, the difference between the digits is 6 – 3 = 3. Then:
3 x 90909 = 272727
636363 – 272727 = 363636

But how did we come up with 90909?
We tried a few examples, such as:
828282 – ? = 282828

Rearranging this sum gave us:
828282 – 282828 = ? = 545454

And another example:
737373 – ? = 373737
737373 – 373737 = ? = 363636

We noticed these numbers are multiples of 9, and that they are related to the difference between the two digits, for example 6 in the first case and 4 in the second case. Dividing these numbers by the difference in the digits gives us 90909 every time.

Root of the problem

• These are the button to press:
2.56 √
Answer: 1.6

Decimal dilemma

• From our knowledge of fractions, it's clear that 3/3 = 1. However, because these decimal equivalents are recurring decimals (they go on forever), this is the closest that the calculator can get to representing them.

A million to 7

• Here are two possible solutions (of which there are many). First:
1,000,000 × 7 = 7,000,000
7,000,000 + 777,777 = 7,777,777
7,777,777 ÷ 7,777,777 = 1
1 × 7 = 7

The second solution shows how calculators cannot store very small numbers, so they round them to zero:
1,000,000 ÷ 77,777,777 = 0.0128571
0.0128571 ÷ 77,777,777 = 0
0 + 7 = 7

pages 12–13 Zoo keeper's conundrum

Feed me – big cats with big appetites!
• 6.8 kg x 5 cats x 7 days x £7.50 = £1,785
• Cheetah: 19 kg x 7 cats x 1 week x £7.50 = £997.50

Tiger: 5.4 kg x 3 cats x 7 days x £7.50 = £850.50

Puma: 4.7 kg x 4 cats x 7 days x £7.50 = £987.00

Jaguar: 20.2 kg x 4 cats x 1 week x £7.50 = £606.00

Answer: £1,785 + £997.5 + £850.5 + £987 + £606 = £5,226.00 per week
• £5,226 x 52 = £271,752.00 per year
• 271,752 + 5% = £285,339.60 per year

How many bags full?

• 7 elephants x 80 kg x 7 days = 3,920 kg (3.920 tonnes) of dung per week
• 1 calf = 40% of 80 kg = 32 kg per day
So 3 x 32 kg x 7 = 672 kg per week
• The number of bags is (3,920 + 672) ÷ 25 = 183.68 bags (183 full bags per week)

Penguin pool puzzle

• 5 x 3 x 1.3 = 19.5 cubic metres (m3)
• 19.5 x 1,000 = 19,500 litres
• 19,500 x 60% = 11,700 litres
• The fence sides will be 7 m and 5 m long, so the perimeter is 7 + 7 + 5 + 5 = 24 m
The number of panels needed is 24 ÷ 1.8 = 13.333333, so we'll need 14 fence panels
• Cost of fence panels: £12 x 14 = £168.00

Tall tales…

• 5.5 m (adult giraffe height) – 2 m (baby giraffe height) = 3.5 metres
• 2 m ÷ 5.5% = 36.363636% (or 36% rounded to the nearest whole number)

- 3.5 ÷ (365 + 365) = 0.0047945 metres

This number is a little difficult to understand, but if we multiply this by 100 we get 0.47945 – that's about half a centimetre per day.

pages 14–15 Patterns and puzzles
Ones and elevens

- $11 \times 11 = 121$

$111 \times 111 = 12321$

$1111 \times 1111 = 1234321$

- $11 \times 111 = 1221$

$11 \times 1111 = 12221$

$11 \times 11111 = 122221$

$11 \times 111111 = 1222221$

$11 \times 1111111 = 12222221$

Whatever next 1?

- $9 \times 9 = 81$

$98 \times 9 = 882$

$987 \times 9 = 8883$

$9876 \times 9 = 88884$

$98765 \times 9 = 888885$

$987654 \times 9 = 8888886$

$9876543 \times 9 = 88888887$

(The last digit is the amount of 8s!)

Whatever next 2?

- $9 - 1 = 8$

$98 - 21 = 77$

$987 - 321 = 666$

$9876 - 4321 = 5555$

$98765 - 54321 = 44444$

$987654 - 654321 = 333333$

$9876543 - 7654321 = 2222222$

$98765432 - 87654321 = 11111111$

Squares

- $11^2 = 121$

$22^2 = 484$

$26^2 = 676$

$101^2 = 10201$

$111^2 = 12321$

$121^2 = 14641$

$202^2 = 40804$

$212^2 = 44944$

$264^2 = 69696$

$307^2 = 94249$

$836^2 = 698896$

$1001^2 = 1002001$

$1111^2 = 1234321$

$2002^2 = 4008004$

$2285^2 = 5221225$

$2636^2 = 6948496$

All the answers are palindromic integers (numbers that read the same backwards and forwards).

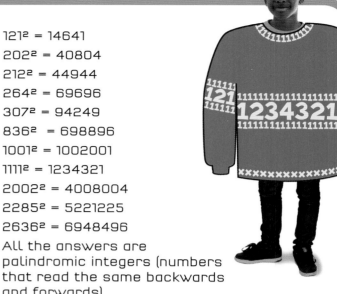

Sum and product

- The two numbers are: 7.2360679 and 2.7639321

This is very difficult! Trial and improvement will give you 7.23 and 2.77 after several attempts. If you are expert at maths you can work it out using a formula that gives a more precise answer of 7.2360679 and 2.7639321.

Find those consecutives!

- Adding three consecutive numbers:

(a) $171 = 56 + 57 + 58$

(b) $210 = 69 + 70 + 71$

(c) $258 = 85 + 86 + 87$

Try this out on your friends. Divide the original number by three, for example $171 \div 3 = 57$. This is the middle one of the three consecutive numbers: 56, 57, and 58!

- The two consecutive numbers with a product of 1332 are 36 and 37.

This is a case of trial and improvement until you reach the correct numbers!

Pick a pair

- ... and subtract:

$74 - 47 = 27$

$52 - 25 = 27$

$63 - 36 = 27$

Is the difference always 27? Yes! The difference between the numbers on the calculator is 3, so when you make a two-digit number the tens differ by 30 and the units differ by 3 (30 – 3 = 27)

- … and add:
20 + 02 = 22
84 + 48 = 132
73 + 37 = 110

What do all the answers have in common? They are all multiples of 11!

When we add the numbers, the sum of the tens is the same as the sum of the units.

pages 16–17 The great bake
All tied up

- 20 – 3 – 5 = 12 cakes are 18 cm in diameter
- 3/20 = 15% are 30 cm in diameter
- Remember that the circumference of a circle = π (or 3.142) x diameter

3 x 3.142 x 30 cm = 282.78 cm

5 x 3.142 x 25 cm = 392.75 cm

12 x 3.142 x 18 cm = 678.672 cm

282.78 + 392.75 + 678.672 + 20 (overlap) = 1,374.202 cm

1,374.202 cm ÷ 100 cm = 13.74 metres

Buy 14 metres of ribbon to be sure.

Pie-portion puzzler

- 8 portions x £1.35 = £10.80 per pie
- £1.35 + 20% = £1.62 per portion
- 12 x £1.62 = £19.44 per pie

£19.44 – £10.80 = £8.64 extra

Cupcakes

- 300 – 132 = 168 more calories
- (3 x 132) + (2.5 x 300) = 1,146 calories
- Total calories low fat cake = 132 x 2 = 264

Total calories normal cake = 300 x 2 = 600

Difference: 600 – 264 = 336 calories

To burn off 336 calories, we need to run:
336 ÷ 95 = 3.5368421 km (about 3.5 km)

Cookie challenge

- 450 + 480 + 675 = 1,605 g (about 1.6 kg)
- 600 ÷ 90 = 6.6666666 chocolate chips per cookie
- 450 x 2/3 = 300 g of butter

480 x 2/3 = 320 g of sugar

675 x 2/3 = 450 g of flour

600 x 2/3 = 400 chocolate chips

Flapjack profit

- It costs £5.50 ÷ 20 = 27.5p per flapjack
- £0.50 x 20 = £10.00 from flapjack sales

£10.00 – £5.50 (cost of ingredients) = £4.50 profit

- £5.50 + 20% = £6.60

£6.60 ÷ 20 = £0.33 (or 33p per flapjack)

pages 18–19 Out of this world!
MIND READING
Pick 1 digit

- The result will be a string of repeated digits. (Ignore the "ERROR" message, which is just the calculator telling you that it can't display the correct answer precisely, since the answer is too long to fit on the display.)

The digit that is repeated will be the one your friend chose at the start!

This is because 9 x 12345679 = 111111111

So, for example, if your friend chooses 4:
4 x 9 x 12345679 = 444444444 (or 4 x 111111111)

Pick 3 digits

- How do you know? Simply remember your friend's original number and write it out twice!

So 437 will become 437437 and 842 will become 842842!

Pick 2 digits

- The answer will always be the two original digits written out three times!

So 38 x 3 x 7 x 13 x 37 = 383838

and 67 x 3 x 7 x 13 x 37 = 676767

An even trickier trick …

- Imagine the original number written out three times, then divide it by three.

So 22 becomes: 222222 ÷ 3 = 74074

And 83 becomes: 838383 ÷ 3 = 279461

It's more difficult to work this trick out, so keep practising – it'll amaze your friends!

EXTRATERRESTRIAL TRICKS

Trick 1

- The answer is always 2!

Trick 2

- The answer is always 3!

Seven-digit surprise!

- You always get the original number!

Golden numbers

- This is an example:

3, 4, 7, 11, 18, 29, 47, 76, 123, 199, 322, 521, 843, 1364, 2207, 3571, 5778, 9349, 15127, 24476, 39603, 64079, 103682, 167761, 271443

271443 ÷ 167761 = 1.6180339

167761 ÷ 103682 = 1.6180339

The golden ratio is a special number that is approximately equal to 1.62. It occurs in several areas of maths, especially geometry, and it also appears in art and architecture.

pages 20–21 School Sports Day
Keep hydrated!

- There 1,000 millilitres in a litre.

So 488 x 25 ÷ 1,000 = 12.2 litres

- (300 + 25) x 488 ÷ 1,000 = 158.6 litres

- We know that 12.2 of squash are needed, so:

12.2 ÷ 0.75 = 16.266666 bottles

The teacher must buy 17 bottles.

On your marks!

- 26 ÷ 4 = 6.5 km
- 95 x 800 ÷ 1,000 = 76 calories
- 1/26 = 0.0384615 hours

To work this out in minutes, multiply by 60:
0.0384615 x 60 = 2.30769 minutes

This is 2 minutes and 0.30769 minutes.

To convert 0.30769 minutes into seconds, multiply by 60:
0.30769 x 60 = 18.4614 seconds

Answer: 2 minutes 18.46 seconds

Big throw

- 24 ÷ 1.2 = 20 lengths

- (37 x 24) x 2 = 1,776 metres (remember the teacher has to walk there and back).

- Second place: 32 m + 6% = 33.92 m
First place: 33.92 m + 10% = 37.312 m

Long leap
- Hop: 35% of 12.8 m = 4.48 m
Skip: 5/6 of 4.48 m = 3.733333 m
Jump: 12.8 – (4.48 + 3.733333) = 4.586667 m

High Jump

- Second place: 160 x 15/16 = 150 cm
Third place: 150 x 7/8 = 131.25 cm
Altogether: (160 + 150 + 131.25) ÷ 100 = 4.4125 m

Take me to your leader!

pages 22-23 Be a calculator detective!
Writing with numbers
- Here are a few examples of words you you can make:

808 = BOB
818 = BIB
616 = GIG
515 = SIS
5335 = SEES
8008 = BOOB
50705 = SOLOS
0.7734 = hello
577345 = shells
35336 = geese
53045 = shoes
77345663 = eggshell

Birthday sleuth
- The way the operations are applied always gives you the answer you are looking for – astonishing, isn't it?

I can tell your age
- As above, the way the operations are applied always gives you the answer you are looking for. Your friends will be amazed!

Symbols mystery
- (37 x 21) + 223 = 1000

(756 ÷ 18) x 29 = 1218

27 + (36 x 18) = 675

31 x (87 – 19) = 2108

We're counting on you to crack the case!
- 123 x 45 = 5535

245 x 13 = 3185

432 x 51 = 22032

- 36 + 89 = 125

Four possible answers: 107 – 68 = 39,
107 – 39 = 68, 107 – 69 = 38, or 107 – 38 = 69

pages 24-25 All the fun of the fair!
You're on a roll!
- 1/6 x 1/6 x 1/6 x 1/6 x 1/6 x 1/6 = 1/46656 chance of winning the car

Or 0.0000214 chance

If they charge £1 a go, the stall's owners will earn an average of £46,656 for each car that is won!

Spend, spend, spend!
- Price of candy floss: 1/3 x £1.20 = £0.40 (or 40p) per portion
- Price of ghost train: £1.20 – 25% = £0.90 (or 90p) per ride
- Price of waltzers: £1.20 + (£1.20 x 1/6) = £1.40 per ride
- Cost of all rides: (2 x £1.20) + (3 x £0.90) + £1.40 + (4 x £0.40) = £8.10

Change from £20: £20 – £8.10 = £11.90

Fancy your chances?
- 1 ÷ 8 = 1 in 8 or 0.125 or 12.5% chance
- 1/8 x 1/7 x 1/6 = 1/336 = 0.0029761 (we are assuming the balls are not replaced after each selection, so the chance improves with each ball you take out)
- 3/8 x 2/7 x 1/6 = 0.0178571 (this is 6 times more likely to occur than picking the balls in a particular order)

Big wheel, big thrills
- 75 ÷ 15 = 5 people per pod
- Remember that the circumference of a circle = π (or 3.142) x diameter

The diameter of a circle is twice its radius, so the diameter of the wheel is 10 metres.

Distance travelled = 3.142 x 10 m x 30 spins = 942.6 metres

- Remember: Speed = Distance ÷ Time

Distance = 942.6 metres (0.9426 km)

Time = 5 ÷ 60 = 0.0833333 hours

To calculate speed: 0.9426 ÷ 0.0833333 = 11.311204 km per hour (about 11 km per hour)

Handy hints and tips
These tips, formulas, units, explanations, and definitions will help you with your calculations.

Commas in numbers

Commas make big numbers easier to read by grouping digits into threes. For example:

123,456,789

From the right-hand side, the first group of three represents hundreds, the second group of three thousands, and the third group of three millions. So the number above is one hundred and twenty three million, four hundred and fifty six thousand, seven hundred and eighty nine.

Average (mean)

To find the average (mean) of a group of numbers, add all the numbers together and divide by how many numbers you have got.

So the average of 1, 2, 3, 4, and 5 is:

$(1 + 2 + 3 + 4 + 5) \div 5 = 3$

Circles and pi (π)

Pi is a number that represents the ratio of a circle's circumference to its diameter. Mathematicians write it as **π**, and it is equal to **3.142**.

To find the circumference of a circle, use the formula: π x diameter.

The diameter is twice the radius, so the formula can also be written: 2πr (2 x π x r).

Equations of Speed, Distance, and Time

Speed = Distance ÷ Time

Time = Distance ÷ Speed

Distance = Speed x Time

Perimeter, area, and volume

The perimeter of a shape is the length of all its sides added together.

To calculate area:
multiply length by width.

To calculate volume:
multiply length by width by depth.

Squared numbers

When you see a number like 3^2, it means multiply the number by itself, in this case 3 x 3. Another example is 6^2, which is 6 x 6.

Product

The product of two numbers is what you get when you multiply them together. For example, the product of 12 and 3, or 12 x 3, equals 36.

Consecutive numbers

Consecutive numbers are numbers that follow on from one another; for example 6 and 7, or 122 and 123.

Probability

The probability of throwing a certain number on a dice, such as 3, is one in six. This is sometimes written as 1/6.

Metric units

Length:

1,000 millimetres (mm) = 1 metre (m)

100 centimetres (cm) = 1 metre (m)

1,000 metres (m) = 1 kilometre (km)

Volume:

1,000 millilitres (ml) = 1 litre

100 centilitres (cl) = 1 litre

1 cubic metre (m3) = 1,000 litres

Weight:

1,000 grams (g) = 1 kilogram (kg)

We still haven't been fed yet!